Then Lesiba found himself a job in Johannesburg. This is when things started to go wrong.

3·50

Mosima makes a plan

written by Monica Rakoma

illustrated by Jeff Rankin

Translated from the original *Sepedi*
by Monica Rakoma

NEW READERS PUBLISHERS

Mosima was married to Lesiba. She was a beautiful woman who was loved by many men. Lesiba was very proud of his wife.

Mosima's many boyfriends came to her house. Thabo was one of them. He did not work and he liked to drink.

Karabo was another one of Mosima's boyfriends. He was a bricklayer in the village.

One day Lesiba decided to go home.
He did not tell Mosima. "I want to
surprise her. Hey! It will be so nice
when I get home," Lesiba said happily
to himself. He wrapped gifts that he
had bought for his wife.

That day Mosima invited Thabo to spend the night with her. They were sitting on the sofa. They were relaxed and happy.

Suddenly they heard a voice at the door. "Mosima, open the door. I am home!" Mosima recognised her husband's voice. She jumped with fright.

Quickly she pulled out a big sack and said to Thabo, "Get inside quickly. Lesiba is here!"

Thabo did not wait. He was frightened. He got inside the sack and Mosima put it behind the door.

Lesiba came in smiling. He did not notice anything wrong. He started telling Mosima about his job. She was happy with the gifts that Lesiba had brought for her. Mosima tried to relax, but she was worried.

After a while somebody knocked at the door. Mosima jumped up to open the door. "Is that you, Karabo? Come in and take away this sack of yours," she said. She did not give Karabo a chance to talk. She gave him a sign with her eyes to warn him that her husband was there.

Karabo picked up the sack with Thabo in it and carried it away.

He complained about the heavy sack. "Women! I walked all the way here for nothing. And now I am carrying a heavy sack in the middle of the night."

"You are better off than I am, because you can see where you are going. What about me?" said a voice from the sack.

Karabo got such a fright he dropped the sack and ran away.

THE END

Thanks

We thank the following people for their help in evaluating the original *Sepedi* version of this story:

Modupi Palane (facilitator), Jane Maake, Joseph Sekgobela, Nurse Mdluli, Sara Letseparela, Tiny Maluleke, Josephina Mokalena, Florah Moswedi, Welhemina Makgate, Elsie Molapo, Salome Moswedi, Josephina Mohlafase and Jerida Machetela from Lesedi Community Development Association, Lephepane, Tzaneen.

Jeffrey Moagi (facilitator), Melita Mogoboya, Maria Malatjie, Agnes Machethe, Anah Malatjie, Janet Seoka, Rachel Makgoba, Josphinah Malatjie, Albertinah Malabela, Rosinah Manyake and Joyce Matlala from Ithusheng Community Association, Lenyenye, Tzaneen.

We thank the following people for their help in evaluating the English version of this story:

Shelley Seid (facilitator), Emily Dladla, Constance Mthembu, Dudu Laza, Armstrong Nkomo, Jabulile Sibisi and Xoliswa Hulley from the University of Natal Adult Literacy Programme.

Monica Rakoma

Monica Rakoma is a lecturer in Adult Education at the University of the North and started working in this field in 1998. She believes that more books should be published in indigenous languages, and intends to write more stories in *Sepedi* for the development of the adult learner population's reading, writing and speaking skills.

NEW READERS PUBLISHERS

New Readers Publishers is a non-profit publishing project based in the School of Community Development and Adult Learning at the University of Natal in Durban. The aim of the project is to contribute to an increase in adult literacy and the promotion of a reading culture. It does this by developing and publishing easy readers in all of South Africa's official languages and by increasing the capacity of teachers through training. The books are read for education and entertainment in first or additional languages.

New Readers Publishers is supported by Rockefeller Brothers Fund.

How to contact us

If you want to find out more about New Readers Publishers or about other books that we publish, please contact:

New Readers Publishers
School of Community Development and Adult Learning
University of Natal
Durban
4041

Tel: 031 – 2602568
Fax: 031 – 2601168
E-mail: keyser@nu.ac.za
Website: www.nrp.und.ac.za

Mosima makes a plan
English version first published 2002 by
New Readers Publishers
School of Community Development and Adult Learning
University of Natal, Durban 4041
South Africa

Translated from **Maano ga a šite** (*Sepedi*)

Cover illustration by Jeff Rankin
Design and desktop publication by Lesley Lewis of Inkspots, Durban
Printed by Interpak Books, Pietermaritzburg

ISBN: 1-86840-482-X